A Word a Day – Over 365 Words

MY STICKER
DICTIONARY

STONEWAY
BOOKS

Published by Stoneway Books
P.O. Box 548, Southeastern, PA 19399

Created and manufactured by arrangement with Otten...
Copyright © 1989 by Ottenh...
Printed in Singapore

My Sticker Words

alarm	farm	milk	rope
ambulance	feather	mittens	sail
apple	fire	money	scissors
aquarium	flag	monkey	shell
bag	foot	napkin	shoe
bandage	frog	necklace	soap
bed	fruit	newspaper	socks
bicycle	gift	nurse	star
book	girl	octopus	strawberry
boots	goat	orange	suitcase
box	grapes	pail	television
bread	hamburger	paint	tomato
button	hand	paper	turkey
cake	heart	pear	turtle
car	horse	piano	umbrella
cat	house	pig	underwear
cheese	ice	pillow	valentine
clown	iron	pool	volcano
cow	kangaroo	popcorn	watch
cup	key	queen	watermelon
dinosaur	ladybug	quilt	whale
dog	lemon	raccoon	whistle
dress	lion	radio	window
drum	lips	rainbow	xylophone
earth	magnet	ring	yarn
elephant			

acorn

An **acorn** is the seed of an oak tree. Squirrels like to eat **acorns**.

addition

Addition is counting things together. One plus one is an **addition** problem.

alarm

An **alarm** is a loud noise. The **alarm** clock wakes you up.

alligator

An **alligator** is a long, dangerous animal with sharp teeth. **Alligators** live in rivers.

ambulance

An **ambulance** is a car that takes people to the hospital. The **ambulance** sped down the street.

anchor

An **anchor** is a heavy piece of metal that keeps boats from moving. The **anchor** is in the water.

ankle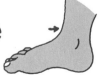

The **ankle** connects the foot and the leg. Your **ankle** lets you move your foot.

ant

An **ant** is a tiny insect. The **ant** crawled on the picnic tablecloth.

Aa

apple   An **apple** is a round fruit that grows on trees. A juicy red **apple** is delicious.

apron 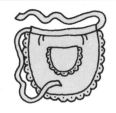 An **apron** is a cloth that keeps your clothes clean. A cook wears an **apron** over her dress.

aquarium   An **aquarium** is a home for fish. There are many colorful fish swimming in the **aquarium**.

arm  The **arm** is a part of the body. Your **arm** is between your shoulder and your wrist.

arrow   An **arrow** is a pointed stick. The Indian hunted with a bow and **arrow**.

astronaut  An **astronaut** is a space traveler. The rocket carried the **astronaut** to the moon.

autumn   **Autumn** is the season when leaves fall. In **autumn** the leaves turn red, orange and yellow.

ax  An **ax** is a tool for chopping wood. The man used his **ax** to cut down the tree.

baby

A **baby** is a very young boy or girl. The mother rocked the **baby** to sleep.

bacon

Bacon is meat from a pig. I had **bacon** and eggs for breakfast.

bag

A **bag** is used to carry things. We carry our groceries home in a **bag**.

ball

A **ball** is a round toy. It is fun to play catch with a **ball**.

balloon

A **balloon** is a bag filled with air. The bright red **balloon** floated in the air.

banana

A **banana** is a curved yellow fruit. The monkey ate the **banana**, peel and all.

bandage

A **bandage** is a strip of cloth to put over a cut. The doctor wrapped a **bandage** around the boy's arm.

barn

A **barn** is a building for farm animals. There are horses and cows in the **barn**.

Bb

basket

A **basket** is used to carry things. Mother carried the eggs in a **basket**.

---

bat

A **bat** is a thick wooden stick. The boy hit the ball with his **bat**.

---

bed

A **bed** is a place to sleep. It's time to go to **bed**.

---

bee

A **bee** is an insect that makes honey. The **bee** buzzed as it flew from flower to flower.

---

bell

A **bell** is something that rings. When the teacher rings the **bell**, the children are quiet.

---

bicycle

A **bicycle** is a toy to ride with two wheels. I am learning to ride a **bicycle**.

---

bird

A **bird** is a feathered animal that can fly. The **bird** flew to the tree and chirped merrily.

---

blanket ·

A **blanket** is a warm cover. You put a **blanket** on a bed.

block  A **block** is a piece of wood. The baby played with the alphabet **blocks.**

boat A **boat** carries you across the water. A large **boat** is called a ship.

bone  A **bone** is the hard part of a body. A skeleton shows all the **bones** in a body.

book A **book** has pages with writing and pictures on them. This **book** is a sticker picture dictionary.

boots  **Boots** are shoes that cover the feet and part of the legs. You wear **boots** when it rains or snows.

bottle A **bottle** is a container for something you can pour. Milk and juice come in **bottles.**

box 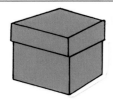 A **box** is a container with flat sides. The children put their toys away in the toy **box.**

boy A **boy** is a male child. When a **boy** grows up, he becomes a man.

Bb

bread

Bread is a food made from flour. **Bread** comes in a loaf.

bridge

A **bridge** is a road over water. We walked across the **bridge.**

broom

A **broom** is a brush with a long handle. You use a **broom** to sweep the floor.

brush

A **brush** is a tool with bristles. I use a **brush** on my hair.

bug

A **bug** is an insect. Ants and bees are **bugs.**

bus

A **bus** is transportation that carries many people. We rode a **bus** downtown.

butterfly

A **butterfly** is an insect with colorful wings. A caterpillar turns into a **butterfly.**

button

A **button** is used to fasten clothes. The tailor sewed a **button** on the coat.

cage
A **cage** is a place made of bars or wire in which to keep an animal. The bird is in the **cage.**

cake
A **cake** is a sweet baked food made from a batter. Mother made a **cake** for my birthday.

camel
A **camel** is an animal with humps on its back. **Camels** live in the desert.

camera
A **camera** is used to take pictures. Daddy took pictures of our family vacation with his **camera.**

candle
A **candle** is a stick of wax that you can light. We lit a **candle** when the lights went out.

canoe
A **canoe** is a small light boat. A **canoe** is moved by hand with paddles or oars.

car
A **car** is something in which we ride. It's fun to go for a ride in the **car.**

carrot
A **carrot** is a long orange vegetable. The rabbit nibbled a **carrot.**

Cc castle

A **castle** is a big building with thick stone walls. The king and queen live in the **castle.**

cat

A **cat** is a small furry animal. When a **cat** is happy, it makes a purring sound.

chair

A **chair** is a piece of furniture with a seat and a back. Daddy sat in his **chair** and read a book.

cheese

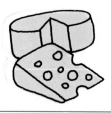

Cheese is a food made from milk. I like **cheese** on crackers.

cherry

A **cherry** is a small red fruit. We picked **cherries** from the tree and made a **cherry** pie.

chimney

A **chimney** is an opening from the fireplace to the roof to let smoke out. This **chimney** is brick.

church

A **church** is a building where you pray. On Sunday, my family went to **church.**

circle

A **circle** is a round shape. The sun is shaped like a **circle.**

clown

A **clown** is a funny person at the circus. The children laughed at the **clown.**

comb

A **comb** is used to smooth or arrange your hair. A **comb** can get the tangles out of your hair.

corn

Corn is a grain with yellow kernels. **Corn** grows on a cob.

cow

A **cow** is a farm animal that gives milk. We also get meat from a **cow.**

crab

A **crab** is a small sea animal with a shell. **Crabs** are good to eat.

crayon

A **crayon** is a colored stick of wax. You can draw and color with **crayons.**

cup

A **cup** is a small container with a handle. You can drink from a **cup.**

cupcake

A **cupcake** is a small cake. The children baked a batch of **cupcakes.**

Dd

daisy

A **daisy** is a flower with petals. The girl picked some **daisies** from the field.

desert

A **desert** is a hot sandy area of land. It's hard to find water in the **desert.**

desk

A **desk** is a table where you read or write. Mother works at her **desk.**

diamond

A **diamond** is a sparkling jewel. It costs a lot of money to buy a **diamond** ring.

dinosaur

A **dinosaur** is an animal that lived long ago. We saw giant **dinosaur** bones at the museum.

dish

A **dish** is used to hold food. Put the **dish** on the table.

doctor

A **doctor** takes care of you when you are sick or hurt. The **doctor** gave me medicine for my cough.

dog

A **dog** is an animal that barks. A **dog** likes to run and play catch.

doll

A **doll** is a toy that looks like a person. The little girl dressed her baby **doll.**

donkey

A **donkey** is an animal that looks like a small horse. A **donkey** has long ears.

door

A **door** is an opening that allows us to enter or leave a place. Daddy came in the front **door.**

dragon

A **dragon** is an imaginary animal that breathes fire. A **dragon** looks like a giant lizard with wings.

dress

A **dress** is a piece of clothing worn by girls and women. She has on a pretty **dress.**

drive

To **drive** is to push something forward to make it go. The bus **driver drives** the bus.

drum

A **drum** is a musical instrument. You beat a **drum** with sticks or your hands.

duck

A **duck** is a bird that can swim. A **duck** has a wide bill and a short neck.

Ee

eagle

An **eagle** is a large fierce bird. An **eagle** makes its nest high on a mountain top.

ear

The **ear** is the part of the body that hears. We use our **ears** to listen to many things.

earth

The **earth** is the planet on which we live. Many, many people live on the **earth.**

egg

An **egg** is what birds and animals lay. A hen's **egg** is good to eat.

elbow

The **elbow** is the part of the arm that bends. Your **elbow** is in the middle of your arm.

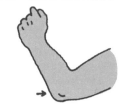

elephant

An **elephant** is a large gray animal with a trunk. We fed peanuts to the **elephant** at the zoo.

eraser

An **eraser** is something that rubs marks away. The boy used an **eraser** on his paper.

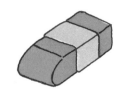

eye

The **eye** is the part of the body that sees. The boy wears glasses because his **eyes** are weak.

face

The **face** is the front part of the head. Your **face** shows whether you are happy or sad.

fairy

A **fairy** is a magical person in stories. A **fairy** has a wand and can grant wishes.

family

A **family** is a mother, a father and their children. This **family** lives in a big brown house.

fan

A **fan** is a machine that blows cool air. Turn on the **fan** if you get too hot.

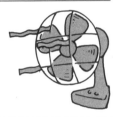

farm

A **farm** is a place where animals are raised and food is grown. We saw cows and pigs at the **farm.**

fat

Fat means big and round. When you eat too much, you get **fat.**

feather

A **feather** is part of the covering on a bird's skin. A parrot has many colorful **feathers.**

fence

A **fence** is a wall around a garden or field. We have a **fence** around our back yard.

Ff fern

A **fern** is a kind of plant. We have a **fern** hanging in our house.

finger

A **finger** is part of the hand. A **fingernail** is the hard part at the end of each **finger.**

fire

A **fire** is something that burns with flames and smoke. **Fire** gives off heat and light.

fireman

A **fireman** is a person who puts out fires. The **fireman** told us never to play with matches.

fish

A **fish** is an animal that lives and breathes in water. Tuna is a **fish** that is good to eat.

fist

A **fist** is a tightly closed hand. Sometimes you hit a ball with your **fist.**

flag

A **flag** is colored cloth on a pole. A **flag** is a symbol of a country or organization.

float

To **float** is to ride on top of the water. I can **float** in the pool.

flower

A **flower** is the blossom of a plant. **Flowers** are pretty to look at.

foot

A **foot** is the part of the body at the end of the leg. Daddy has a big **foot.**

footprint

A **footprint** is the mark that a foot makes. Daddy makes big **footprints** when he walks in the snow.

fork

A **fork** is a tool with which you eat. I eat cake with a **fork.**

fox

A **fox** is a wild animal that looks like a dog. A **fox** has pointy ears and a bushy tail.

frog

A **frog** is a small animal that lives in or near the water. **Frogs** hop from place to place.

fruit

A **fruit** is the part of a plant that you can eat. The bowl is filled with **fruit.**

fur

Fur is the hair that covers an animal. Mother's coat is made of **fur.**

Gg

garden

A **garden** is a place to grow vegetables or flowers. We planted seeds in our **garden.**

---

gate

A **gate** is the door in a fence. Be sure to close the **gate** so the dog can't run out.

---

ghost

A **ghost** is a spirit. We heard a scary **ghost** story on Halloween.

---

gift

A **gift** is a present given to someone. The birthday **gift** was wrapped in pretty paper and ribbon.

---

giraffe

A **giraffe** is a tall animal with a very long neck. A **giraffe** has spots on its skin.

---

girl

A **girl** is a female child. When a **girl** grows up, she becomes a woman.

---

glass

A **glass** is a container from which to drink. I had a **glass** of milk and some cookies.

---

glove

A **glove** is something worn on the hand. **Gloves** have parts to cover each finger.

glue  **Glue** is a paste that sticks things together. **Gg**
Daddy used **glue** to fix my doll.

goat A **goat** is a farm animal with horns.
Goats like to eat grass.

goose  A **goose** is a long-necked bird that looks
like a duck. We use **goose** feathers to stuff
pillows.

gown A **gown** is a long dress worn by a woman.
The princess wore a beautiful **gown.**

grapes  **Grapes** are fruits that grow on vines. Dried
grapes are called raisins.

grasshopper A **grasshopper** is a green
insect. A **grasshopper** has long
back legs for jumping.

guitar  A **guitar** is a musical instrument with strings. The
singer plucked his **guitar** and sang a song.

gull A **gull** is a bird that lives near the water. We
saw a **gull** at the ocean.

Hh

hair   Hair is what grows on animals' skin. You have **hair** on your head.

hamburger      A **hamburger** is a patty of ground beef. For supper I had a juicy **hamburger** on a bun.

hammer   A **hammer** is a tool for hitting nails. Daddy has a **hammer** in his toolbox.

hand      A **hand** is the part of the body at the end of the arm. Your **hand** has five fingers.

hanger   A **hanger** is something on which to hang clothes. My coat is on a **hanger** in the closet.

hat      A **hat** is a covering for the head. A **hat** keeps your head warm on a cold day.

heart   A **heart** is the shape of a valentine. I can make a pretty **heart** from red paper.

helicopter      A **helicopter** is a type of aircraft. The **helicopter** landed on the roof of the building.

hen  A **hen** is a mother chicken. The **hen** laid four eggs.

hill A **hill** is a small mountain. We climbed up the **hill.**

hole  A **hole** is a hollow place in something solid. I have **holes** in my socks.

honey **Honey** is a sweet syrup made by bees. The bear cub found a hive full of **honey.**

hop  To **hop** is to jump up and down on one foot. You have to **hop** when you play hopscotch.

horn A **horn** is an instrument that you blow. When you blow very hard, the **horn** makes a loud noise.

horse  A **horse** is a strong animal with four legs and a long tail. I rode a **horse** in the field.

house A **house** is a building where people live. A **house** has many rooms.

Ii

ice

Ice is frozen water. We put **ice** cubes in drinks to keep them cold.

ice cream

Ice cream is a sweet frozen dessert. I had **ice cream** in a cone.

icicle

An **icicle** is formed when dripping water freezes. An **icicle** hung from the tree branch.

igloo

An **igloo** is a house made from blocks of snow. Eskimos live in **igloos.**

ink

Ink is colored liquid used for writing. Daddy filled his pen with blue **ink.**

iris

An **iris** is a colorful flower. A beautiful **iris** grew in our garden.

iron

An **iron** is used to press clothes smooth. Mother used an **iron** to take the creases out of my dress.

island

An **island** is land with water all around it. There were palm trees on the **island.**

jacket  A **jacket** is a short coat. This is a good **jacket** to wear on a chilly day.

jack-o'-lantern A **jack-o'-lantern** is a pumpkin with a carved face. We see **jack-o'-lanterns** at Halloween.

jellyfish  A **jellyfish** is a soft rubbery fish. We saw many **jellyfish** at the beach.

jumprope A **jumprope** is a rope with handles. You can play jumping games with a **jumprope.**

kangaroo  A **kangaroo** is an animal with strong back legs for jumping. Mother **kangaroo** carries baby in her pouch.

key A **key** is a piece of metal that turns a lock to open or close it. I have a **key** to my front door.

king  A **king** is a man who rules a country. The **king** wears a crown and sits on a throne.

kite A **kite** is a toy that you can fly. You need a windy day to fly a **kite.**

Ll

ladder

A **ladder** is used to reach high places. Daddy climbed a **ladder** to reach the roof.

ladybug

A **ladybug** is a small round insect. A **ladybug** is red with black spots.

lamb

A **lamb** is a baby sheep. A **lamb** has soft curly wool.

lantern

A **lantern** is a lamp you can carry. We use a **lantern** when the lights go out during a storm.

leaves

Leaves are parts of a plant. There are many **leaves** on a tree.

leg

A **leg** is part of the body. You can stand and walk on your two **legs.**

lemon

A **lemon** is a sour yellow fruit. You can make lemonade with **lemons,** water and sugar.

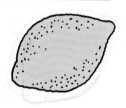

lettuce

Lettuce is a vegetable with green leaves. The salad was made with **lettuce** and tomatoes.

lighthouse

A **lighthouse** is a tower with a light on top. A **lighthouse** helps ships on the dark sea.

lightning

Lightning is a flash of light in the sky. You see **lightning** during a storm.

lion

A **lion** is a strong wild cat. A male **lion** has a mane of fur around its head and neck.

lips

Lips are part of the face. You have two **lips** around your mouth.

lobster

A **lobster** is a sea animal with claws and a hard shell. We saw **lobsters** in a fish tank.

lock

A **lock** is a fastener that keeps things closed. You need a key to un**lock** a **lock.**

log

A **log** is a piece of wood cut from a tree. You use **logs** in a fireplace.

lollipop

A **lollipop** is candy on a stick. The little girl licked the **lollipop.**

Mm

magnet

A **magnet** is a special kind of metal. A **magnet** has the power to pull iron or steel to it.

map

A **map** is a drawing that shows places on the earth's surface. We use a **map** when we go on a trip.

marshmallow

A **marshmallow** is a soft white candy. I like **marshmallows** in my hot chocolate.

maze

A **maze** is a type of puzzle. To do a **maze** you must follow a path without crossing any lines.

meat

Meat is food from animals. Both steak and lamb chops are **meat.**

milk

Milk is a white drink that comes from cows. **Milk** gives you strong bones and teeth.

mittens

Mittens are coverings for the hands. **Mittens** keep your hands warm when you play in the snow.

moccasins

Moccasins are soft leather shoes. Indians wear **moccasins.**

mole  A **mole** is a small animal that digs tunnels in the ground. These holes were made by a **mole.**

money **Money** is coins or paper used to buy things. I spent my **money** on a new toy.

monkey  A **monkey** is an animal that is a good climber. **Monkeys** swing from branches by their long tails.

moon The **moon** is a heavenly body that shines at night. There is a crescent **moon** in the sky.

moose  A **moose** is a large animal with antlers on its head. A **moose** looks like a deer.

mouse A **mouse** is a small animal. A **mouse** has a long thin tail.

mushroom A **mushroom** is a plant that grows in a wet place. **Mushrooms** look like small umbrellas.

mustache A **mustache** is hair that grows above a man's lip. My father has a **mustache.**

Nn

nail

A **nail** is a thin piece of metal with a pointed end. We put a **nail** in the wall to hang a picture.

nap

A **nap** is a short sleep. The girl took an afternoon **nap.**

napkin

A **napkin** is a piece of cloth or paper used at meals to keep clean. He had a **napkin** around his neck.

neck

The **neck** is part of the body. The **neck** connects the head and shoulders.

necklace

A **necklace** is a chain or beads worn around the neck. She had on a pretty **necklace.**

necktie

A **necktie** is a cloth a man wears around his neck. We gave father a **necktie** for Christmas.

needle

A **needle** is a thin piece of metal. A **needle** has a hole at one end for thread.

nest

A **nest** is a home made by birds. Birds lay their eggs in a **nest.**

net

A **net** is an open cloth of strings used to catch things. Fishermen use **nets.**

newspaper

A **newspaper** has printed sheets of paper that contain news. We get a **newspaper** every day.

night

Night is the time when it is dark outside. The moon and stars shine at **night.**

nipple

A **nipple** is the rubber tip of a baby's bottle. The baby sucked milk through the **nipple.**

nose

The **nose** is part of the face. You breathe and smell things through your **nose.**

numbers

Numbers are used for counting. I can count **numbers** up to fifty.

nurse

A **nurse** is a person who takes care of sick people. A **nurse** works in a hospital.

nut

A **nut** is a food with a hard shell. Walnuts and almonds are **nuts.**

Oo

oar

An **oar** is a stick used to row a boat. The rowboat has two **oars.**

ocean

An **ocean** is a large body of salty water. Ships sail across the **ocean.**

octopus

An **octopus** is a sea animal with eight legs. An **octopus** lives in the dark bottom of the ocean.

olive

An **olive** is a small green fruit. **Olive** oil is made by squeezing **olives.**

onion

An **onion** is a vegetable with a spicy taste. The smell of an **onion** makes your eyes fill with tears.

orange

An **orange** is a round **orange** fruit. A sweet juicy **orange** is delicious and good for you.

ostrich

An **ostrich** is a big bird with a long neck. An **ostrich** cannot fly, but its long legs run very fast.

owl

An **owl** is a bird with big round eyes. The **owl** sleeps during the day and hunts for food at night.

pail  A **pail** is a bucket with a handle. I played with a **pail** and shovel at the beach.

paint **Paint** is a mixture that is used to color things. I used many colors of **paint** for my picture.

pair  A **pair** is two things that go together. We have a **pair** of shoes because we have two feet.

pajamas **Pajamas** are clothes that you wear when you sleep. Put on your **pajamas** and get ready for bed.

pan  A **pan** is a metal dish with a handle for cooking food. Mother fried eggs in the **pan.**

pancake A **pancake** is a thin flat cake. **Pancakes** are good with butter and syrup on them.

pants  **Pants** are clothes that cover the body below the waist. The little boy wore a new pair of **pants.**

paper **Paper** is material used for writing and printing. Write your name at the top of the **paper.**

Pp

parrot

A **parrot** is a bird with colorful feathers.
A **parrot** can learn to talk.

pea

A **pea** is a small, round, green vegetable.
Peas grow in pods.

peanut

A **peanut** is a food with a soft shell.
Peanut butter is made from ground
peanuts.

pear

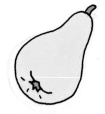

A **pear** is a fruit with an oval shape. **Pears**
grow on trees.

pen

A **pen** is a tool for writing in ink. Daddy
uses a **pen** when he works.

pencil

A **pencil** is a thin stick of wood with lead in
it. I wrote my name with a **pencil.**

piano

A **piano** is a musical instrument played
with the fingers. A **piano** has black and
white keys.

picnic

A **picnic** is a meal that you eat outside. We
had a **picnic** in the park.

picture  A **picture** is a drawing or photograph. The **picture** was in a frame. **Pp**

pie A **pie** is a pastry shell filled with fruit or other foods. Mother baked an apple **pie.**

pig  A **pig** is a fat animal with a short snout and a curly tail. Meat from a **pig** is called pork.

pillow A **pillow** is a soft cushion. The little girl put her head on the **pillow.**

pilot  A **pilot** is a person who flies an aircraft. The **pilot** sits in the cockpit.

pipe A **pipe** is a tube through which gas or liquid moves. Water in a house goes through **pipes.**

pocket  A **pocket** is a place in clothing to hold things. Put the money in your **pocket** so you don't lose it.

pole A **pole** is a long stick. The flag is fastened to a **pole.**

Pp

policeman

A **policeman** protects people. A **policeman** stops traffic so we can cross the street.

pool

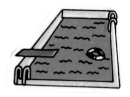

A **pool** is a place to swim. We have a **pool** in our backyard.

popcorn

Popcorn is corn that pops open when it is heated. We ate hot buttered **popcorn** at the movies.

porch

A **porch** is a roofed area built onto a house. We like to sit on the **porch** in the evening.

pot

A **pot** is a round container for cooking. Mother makes soup in a big **pot**.

potato

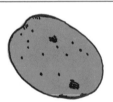

A **potato** is a vegetable that grows under the ground. **Potatoes** are delicious mashed, fried or baked.

pumpkin

A **pumpkin** is a big orange fruit. We see many **pumpkins** at Halloween.

purse

A **purse** is a small bag that a lady carries. Mother keeps her money and keys in a **purse.**

quail  A **quail** is a small brown bird with a short tail. **Quail** can be eaten like chicken.

quart A **quart** is a unit of measurement. The pitcher held a **quart**, or two pints, of milk.

quarter  A **quarter** is one of four equal parts. He ate a **quarter** of the pie.

queen A **queen** is a woman who rules a country. A **queen** lives in a castle.

question A **question** is what you ask in order to learn something. A **question** has an answer.

quicksand **Quicksand** is very deep and wet sand. You will get stuck in **quicksand** if you step in it.

quill  A **quill** is a pointed feather used for writing. Long ago, people used **quill** pens.

quilt A **quilt** is a blanket. A patchwork **quilt** is made from many pieces of cloth.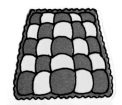

Rr

rabbit   A **rabbit** is an animal with long ears. **Rabbits** can hop very fast.

raccoon    A **raccoon** is an animal with black circles around its eyes. **Raccoons** look for food at night.

race   A **race** is a contest to see who can go the fastest. The children had a **race.**

radio    A **radio** is a machine that you turn on to hear music or talking. We listen to the **radio** every morning.

rainbow   A **rainbow** is an arch of colors in the sky. A **rainbow** appears when the sun shines after a storm.

raincoat    A **raincoat** is a coat that keeps you dry. Wear a **raincoat** when you walk in the rain.

refrigerator   A **refrigerator** is a machine that keeps food cold. Lots of different foods are in our **refrigerator.**

ribbon    A **ribbon** is a pretty strip of cloth or paper used for decoration. She had a **ribbon** in her hair.

rice  **Rice** is a grain that looks like white seeds. We had **rice** with our dinner.

ring A **ring** is a band that you wear on your finger. Mommy has lots of pretty **rings.**

river  A **river** is a large stream of water. The fish swam down the **river.**

roof A **roof** is the top of a building. The **roof** keeps the rain out.

rope  **Rope** is strong thick cord. The cowboy used a **rope** to catch the calf.

rose A **rose** is a beautiful flower that grows on a bush. **Roses** have soft petals with a sweet smell.

row  To **row** is to move a boat with oars. Can you **row** the boat to the other side of the lake?

ruler A **ruler** is a stick used for measuring. Most **rulers** are twelve inches long.

Ss

sail

A **sail** is a piece of cloth on a boat's mast. Wind blows against the **sail** to make the boat go.

sandwich

A **sandwich** is two slices of bread with filling between them. I had a cheese **sandwich.**

scarf

A **scarf** is a piece of cloth worn around the neck or head. A **scarf** keeps you warm on a cold day.

school

School is a building where you go to learn. There are many classrooms in a **school.**

scissors

Scissors are a tool used for cutting. **Scissors** have two sharp blades and holes for two fingers.

scooter

A **scooter** is a toy to ride with two wheels. You push with your foot to make a **scooter** go.

seal

A **seal** is a sea animal with flippers. **Seals** love to eat fish.

shape

A **shape** is the outside form of something. Circles, squares and triangles are different **shapes.**

Ss

shell

A **shell** is an outside covering for a sea creature. We found many pretty **shells** at the beach.

shoe

A **shoe** is a covering for the foot. **Shoes** protect your feet.

shorts

Shorts are short pants. We wear **shorts** when it is hot.

shovel

A **shovel** is a tool for digging. Father dug a hole with the **shovel.**

sidewalk

A **sidewalk** is the paved path along the side of the road. We walk on the **sidewalk.**

sign

A **sign** tells us something we should know. The **sign** told us which way to go.

skate

A **skate** is a shoe with wheels or a blade. I got a new pair of roller **skates.**

skirt

A **skirt** is clothing worn below the waist by girls and women. Sally wore a new **skirt** today.

Ss

sky

The **sky** is the space above the earth. Clouds float in the **sky.**

slippers

Slippers are soft shoes worn in the house. I put on my pajamas and **slippers.**

smile

A **smile** is a happy face. The little boy greeted his puppy with a big **smile.**

smoke

Smoke is a gray cloud that comes from something burning. **Smoke** came out of the chimney.

snake

A **snake** is a long thin animal with no legs. **Snakes** move by sliding along the ground.

snow

Snow is icy white flakes that fall in winter. We built a **snow**man from **snow.**

soap

Soap is used to clean off dirt. You use **soap** when you take a bath.

socks

Socks are coverings for the feet. **Socks** keep your feet warm and dry inside your shoes.

soup  **Soup** is liquid food. A bowl of hot **soup** is good on a cold day.

spider A **spider** is a small creature with eight legs. A **spider** spins a thin thread called a web.

spoon  A **spoon** is a tool used for eating. You use a **spoon** to eat soup and ice cream.

stairs **Stairs** are steps for going up and down. I go up the **stairs** to get to my bedroom.

stamp 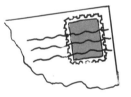 A **stamp** is a small piece of paper with glue on the back. You must put a **stamp** on a letter.

star A **star** is a tiny heavenly body of light we see in the night sky. There are many **stars** in the sky.

strawberry  A **strawberry** is a small red fruit. I like **strawberries** with my cereal.

suitcase A **suitcase** is a flat box with a handle. You carry clothes in a **suitcase** when you go on a trip.

Tt

taxi A **taxi** is a car for which you pay to ride. Dad took a **taxi** to work when his car broke down.

tear  A **tear** is a drop of water that comes from the eye. You cry **tears** when you are very sad.

teeth **Teeth** are used for biting and chewing food. You should brush your **teeth** every day.

telephone  A **telephone** is a way to talk to people who are not near you. I called a friend on the **telephone**.

television A **television** is a machine on which we watch programs. I watch cartoons on **television.**

tent  A **tent** is a small shelter made of cloth. When we went camping, we slept in a **tent.**

toes **Toes** are parts of feet. You have ten **toes,** five on each foot.

tomato  A **tomato** is a round red fruit. **Tomato** sauce and ketchup are made from **tomatoes.**

tongue
A **tongue** is the part of the mouth that tastes food. You lick a lollipop with your **tongue.**

towel
A **towel** is a cloth used for drying things. After my bath I dry myself with a big **towel.**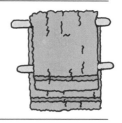

toy
A **toy** is something to play with. A top is a kind of **toy.**

train
A **train** is a row of railroad cars that ride on a track. Some people ride a **train** to work.

truck
A **truck** is used to carry heavy loads. **Trucks** carry the groceries that fill the stores.

tulip
A **tulip** is a brightly-colored flower. **Tulips** are among the first flowers you see in the spring.

turkey
A **turkey** is a big farm bird raised as food. Many people eat **turkey** at Christmas.

turtle
A **turtle** is an animal with a hard shell on its back. **Turtles** move very slowly.

Uu

ugly   **Ugly** means not nice to look at. The monster mask was **ugly**.

umbrella      An **umbrella** is used to keep you dry in the rain. You carry an **umbrella** over your head.

underpass   An **underpass** is a road that goes under another road. We walked along the **underpass**.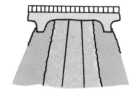

underwear      **Underwear** is clothing worn under your outer clothes. Mother bought me some new **underwear**.

unhappy   **Unhappy** means sad. The little boy was **unhappy** when his balloon burst.

unicorn      A **unicorn** is a make-believe animal that looks like a horse. A **unicorn** has a horn on its head.

unicycle   A **unicycle** is a toy to ride with one wheel. We saw a clown riding a **unicycle** at the circus.

uniform      A **uniform** is special clothing that someone wears for his job. A sailor wears a **uniform**.

vacuum

A **vacuum** is a machine that sucks up dirt. Mother uses the **vacuum** on the carpet.

valentine

A **valentine** is a card you give on Valentine's Day. I made a pretty **valentine** for Mom and Dad.

van

A **van** is a covered truck. Father loaded the **van** with furniture.

vase

A **vase** is a container to hold flowers. We put the fresh flowers in a **vase** with water.

vest

A **vest** is a jacket without sleeves. Grandpa wears a **vest**.

violets

Violets are small wildflowers. We saw **violets** growing in the field.

violin

A **violin** is a stringed musical instrument. You play a **violin** with a bow.

volcano

A **volcano** is an opening in the earth's surface. Inside the **volcano** are burning rocks and hot ashes.

Ww

waffle

A **waffle** is a thin batter cake with little squares. Mother made **waffles** for breakfast.

---

wagon

A **wagon** is something in which to ride or carry things. I have a new red **wagon.**

---

walrus

A **walrus** is a sea animal with two long tusks. We saw a **walrus** swimmming in a pool at the zoo.

---

watch

A **watch** is a small clock you wear on your wrist. A **watch** tells you what time it is.

---

water

Water is the liquid covering the earth. **Water** fills oceans, rivers, lakes, and ponds.

---

watermelon

A **watermelon** is a big fruit with a hard green shell. **Watermelon** has juicy red fruit and many seeds.

---

web

A **web** is a net made by a spider. The spider uses the **web** to catch flies.

---

whale

A **whale** is the biggest animal in the sea. A **whale** looks like a giant fish.

wheat  **Wheat** is a grassy plant whose grain is made into flour. **Wheat** flour is used to make bread and cereal.

wheel A **wheel** is round. A **wheel** turns to help things like cars and bicycles to move.

whistle  A **whistle** is an instrument that makes a sharp sound. The policeman blew the **whistle** to stop the cars.

wigwam A **wigwam** is an Indian tent. Indians make **wigwams** from buffalo skins.

windmill  A **windmill** uses the power of the wind. The wind pushes the **windmill's** blades and makes them turn.

window A **window** is a glass opening in a wall for you to see through. **Windows** let in air and light.

witch  A **witch** is a make-believe person who is wicked and ugly. The **witch** rode her magic broom.

worm A **worm** is a small creature with no legs. Birds like to eat **worms.**

Xx Yy Zz

x-ray

An **x-ray** is a picture that shows the inside of the body. The **x-ray** showed that my foot was broken.

xylophone

A **xylophone** is a musical instrument. You play the **xylophone** with little mallets.

yam

A **yam** is a sweet potato. My mother cooks **yams** with marshmallows.

yarn

Yarn is wool used for knitting. We use **yarn** to make sweaters and scarves.

yo-yo

A **yo-yo** is a toy that looks like a spool with string. A **yo-yo** rolls down the string and spins up again.

zebra

A **zebra** is an animal with black and white stripes. A **zebra** looks like a striped horse.

zipper

A **zipper** is a fastener for clothes. Close the **zipper** on your jacket to keep warm.

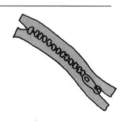

zoo

A **zoo** is a place where different animals are kept. We visit the **zoo** to see wild animals.